# Colour Yourself to
# MINDFULNESS

## 100 mandalas and motifs
## to colour in to reduce stress

**CICO BOOKS**

LONDON  NEW YORK

Published in 2015 by CICO Books
An imprint of Ryland Peters & Small Ltd
20–21 Jockey's Fields    341 E 116th St
London WC1R 4BW    New York, NY 10029
www.rylandpeters.com

10 9 8 7 6 5 4 3

US ISBN (**Color Yourself to Mindfulness**):
978 1 78249 323 5

UK ISBN (**Colour Yourself to Mindfulness**):
978 1 78249 325 9

Printed in China

Illustration: Stephen Dew
Adapted from original artworks by
Melissa Launay

Senior editor: Carmel Edmonds
In-house designer: Fahema Khanam
In-house design assistant: Kerry Lewis
Art director: Sally Powell
Head of production: Patricia Harrington
Publishing manager: Penny Craig
Publisher: Cindy Richards

# CONTENTS

4

PASSION

GROWTH

CHILDHOOD

GRACE

WISDOM

**PLENTY**

MENTOR

SERVICE

DIVINE LOVE

DEVOTION

BELTANE

**MIDSUMMER**

OSTARA

MABON

**WILLOW KNOT**

NEW RELATIONSHIPS

**THE GREEN MAN**

**THE SOLAR WHEEL**

**SUCCESS**

DANCE

NEW JOURNEY

**INVOCATION**

**FORGIVENESS**

GROUNDING

**PAIN**

INTEGRATION

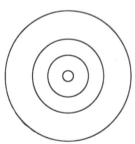

**REACHING OUT**

SELF-ESTEEM

AWARENESS

LAUGHTER

**THE MAZE**

COMMUNICATION

LOSS

HEALING

FLOW

**PLANTING THE SEED**

COMPLETION

**SHRI YANTRA**

# THE HANDS OF GOD

MASCULINITY

CONNECTION

  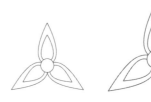

**FLOWER KNOT**

COMPASSION

**TREE OF LIFE**

LOOKING ANEW

ENERGY

KARMA

DEPRESSION

ABUNDANCE

PEACE

COMPANIONSHIP

EARTH

BOREDOM

NEW THINGS

CREATIVITY

KNOWLEDGE

RENEWAL

RELEASE

**PERSONAL POWER**

WATER OF LIFE

GUILT

**NATURE**

RAINBOW

NEW LIFE

**CORNUCOPIA**

RIVERS

DEATH

NEW BEGINNINGS

BLISSFUL DESIRE

**SELF-EXPRESSION**

BONDING

IMPERMANENCE

**LOOKING**

**RITUAL**

LOVE

**WHEEL OF LIFE**

FEMININITY

EARTHLY CONNECTION

CONCEPTION

MOUNTAIN

DEITY ANGEL

GRIEF

WATER

BOUNTIFUL

SUFFERING

**CHILDREN**

**CHAKRA**

**MEDITATION**

# DOODLE YOUR OWN MANDALA

To make your own mandala, sit peacefully and quieten your mind. You can copy the motifs here or from throughout the book. Alternatively, create your own, such as stars, crescent moons, suns, flowers, and shapes linked with the elements (earth, air, fire, and water).

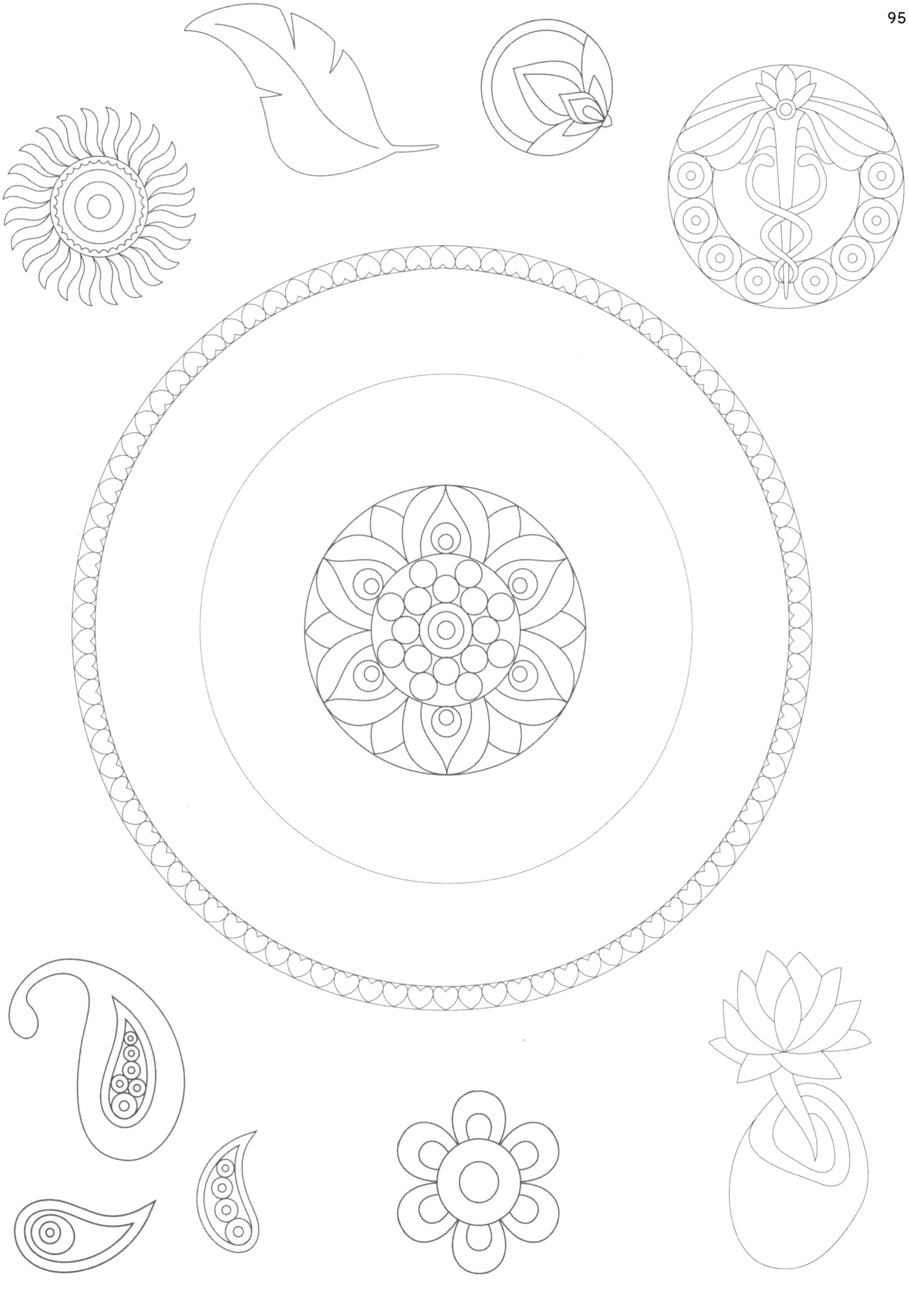